New Jersey State Parks and Forests, A Travel Journal for Families

We must teach our children to smell the earth, to taste the rain, to touch the wind, to see things grow, to hear the sun rise and night fall – to care.

John Cleal

Abram S. Hewitt State Forest

885 Warwick Turnpike, Hewitt

When did you visit?

Who came with you?

What did you do?

What was your favorite part?

Would you want to come back?

Draw or add a picture of Abram S. Hewitt State Forest

Allaire State Park

4265 Atlantic Avenue, Farmingdale

When did you visit?

Who came with you?

What did you do?

What was your favorite part?

Would you want to come back?

Draw or add a picture of Allaire State Park

Allamuchy Mountain State Park

800 Willow Grove Street, Hackettstown

When did you visit?

Who came with you?

What did you do?

What was your favorite part?

Would you want to come back?

Draw or add a picture of Allamuchy Mountain State Park

Atsion Recreation Area

US-206, Wharton State Forest, Shamong

When did you visit?

Who came with you?

What did you do?

What was your favorite part?

Would you want to come back?

Draw or add a picture of Atsion Recreation Area

Barnegat Lighthouse State Park

Barnegat Light

When did you visit?

Who came with you?

What did you do?

What was your favorite part?

Would you want to come back?

Draw or add a picture of Barnegat Lighthouse State Park

Bass River State Forest

762 Stage Road, Tuckerton

When did you visit?

Who came with you?

What did you do?

What was your favorite part?

Would you want to come back?

Draw or add a picture of Bass River State Forest

Belleplain State Forest

1 Henkinsifkin Road, Woodbine

When did you visit?

Who came with you?

What did you do?

What was your favorite part?

Would you want to come back?

Draw or add a picture of Belleplain State Forest

Brendan T. Byrne State Forest

Highway Route 72 East, Woodland Township

When did you visit?

Who came with you?

What did you do?

What was your favorite part?

Would you want to come back?

Draw or add a picture of Brendan T. Byrne State Forest

Bull's Island Recreation Area

2185 Daniel Bray Hwy, Stockton

When did you visit?

Who came with you?

What did you do?

What was your favorite part?

Would you want to come back?

Draw or add a picture of Bull's Island Recreation Area

Cape May Point State Park

Light House Avenue, Cape May Point

When did you visit?

Who came with you?

What did you do?

What was your favorite part?

Would you want to come back?

Draw or add a picture of Cape May Point State Park

Cheesequake State Park

300 Gordon Road, Matawan

When did you visit?

Who came with you?

What did you do?

What was your favorite part?

Would you want to come back?

Draw or add a picture of Cheesequake State Park

Corson's Inlet State Park

6001 Bay Avenue, Ocean City

When did you visit?

Who came with you?

What did you do?

What was your favorite part?

Would you want to come back?

Draw or add a picture of Corson's Inlet State Park

Delaware and Raritan Canal State Park

145 Mapleton Road, Princeton

When did you visit?

Who came with you?

What did you do?

What was your favorite part?

Would you want to come back?

Draw or add a picture of Delaware and Raritan Canal State Park

Double Trouble State Park

581 Pinewald Keswick Road, Forked River

When did you visit?

Who came with you?

What did you do?

What was your favorite part?

Would you want to come back?

Draw or add a picture of Double Trouble State Park

Farny State Park

9-99 Carleys Way, Rockaway

When did you visit?

Who came with you?

What did you do?

What was your favorite part?

Would you want to come back?

Draw or add a picture of Farny State Park

Fort Mott State Park

454 Fort Mott Road, Pennsville

When did you visit?

Who came with you?

What did you do?

What was your favorite part?

Would you want to come back?

Draw or add a picture of Fort Mott State Park

Hacklebarney State Park

119 Hacklebarney Road, Long Valley

When did you visit?

Who came with you?

What did you do?

What was your favorite part?

Would you want to come back?

Draw or add a picture of Hacklebarney State Park

High Point State Park

1480 Route 23, Sussex

When did you visit?

Who came with you?

What did you do?

What was your favorite part?

Would you want to come back?

Draw or add a picture of High Point State Park

Hopatcong State Park

260 Lakeside Boulevard, Roxbury

When did you visit?

Who came with you?

What did you do?

What was your favorite part?

Would you want to come back?

Draw or add a picture of Hopatcong State Park

Island Beach State Park

Ocean Gate

When did you visit?

Who came with you?

What did you do?

What was your favorite part?

Would you want to come back?

Draw or add a picture of Island Beach State Park

Jenny Jump State Forest

281 State Park Road, Blairstown

When did you visit?

Who came with you?

What did you do?

What was your favorite part?

Would you want to come back?

Draw or add a picture of Jenny Jump State Forest

Kittatinny Valley State Park

199 Goodale Road, Newton

When did you visit?

Who came with you?

What did you do?

What was your favorite part?

Would you want to come back?

Draw or add a picture of Kittatinny Valley State Park

Liberty State Park

200 Morris Pesin Drive, Jersey City

When did you visit?

Who came with you?

What did you do?

What was your favorite part?

Would you want to come back?

Draw or add a picture of Liberty State Park

Long Pond IronWorks State Park

Hewitt

When did you visit?

Who came with you?

What did you do?

What was your favorite part?

Would you want to come back?

Draw or add a picture of Long Pond Ironworks State Park

Monmouth Battlefield State Park

16 Business Route 33, Manalapan

When did you visit?

Who came with you?

What did you do?

What was your favorite part?

Would you want to come back?

Draw or add a picture of Monmouth Battlefield State Park

Norvin Green State Forest

Bloomingdale/Wanaque

When did you visit?

Who came with you?

What did you do?

What was your favorite part?

Would you want to come back?

Draw or add a picture of Norvin Green State Forest

Parvin State Park

701 Almond Road, Pittsgrove

When did you visit?

Who came with you?

What did you do?

What was your favorite part?

Would you want to come back?

Draw or add a picture of Parvin State Park

Penn State Forest

Sooey Road, Chatsworth

When did you visit?

Who came with you?

What did you do?

What was your favorite part?

Would you want to come back?

Draw or add a picture of Penn State Forest

Princeton Battlefield State Park

500 Mercer Road, Princeton

When did you visit?

Who came with you?

What did you do?

What was your favorite part?

Would you want to come back?

Draw or add a picture of Princeton Battlefield State Park

Ramapo Mountain State Forest

1304 Sloatsburg Road, Ringwood

When did you visit?

Who came with you?

What did you do?

What was your favorite part?

Would you want to come back?

Draw or add a picture of Ramapo Mountain State Forest

Rancocas State Park

Rancocas Avenue, Hainesport

When did you visit?

Who came with you?

What did you do?

What was your favorite part?

Would you want to come back?

Draw or add a picture of Rancocas State Park

Ringwood State Park

1304 Sloatsburg Road, Ringwood

When did you visit?

Who came with you?

What did you do?

What was your favorite part?

Would you want to come back?

Draw or add a picture of Ringwood State Park

Round Valley Recreation Area

1220 Lebanon–Stanton Road, Lebanon

When did you visit?

Who came with you?

What did you do?

What was your favorite part?

Would you want to come back?

Draw or add a picture of Round Valley Recreation Area

Spruce Run Recreation Area

Spruce Run State Park, Clinton

When did you visit?

Who came with you?

What did you do?

What was your favorite part?

Would you want to come back?

Draw or add a picture of Spruce Run Recreation Area

Stephens State Park

800 Willow Grove Street, Hackettstown

When did you visit?

Who came with you?

What did you do?

What was your favorite part?

Would you want to come back?

Draw or add a picture of Stephens State Park

Stokes State Forest

1 Coursen Road, Branchville

When did you visit?

Who came with you?

What did you do?

What was your favorite part?

Would you want to come back?

Draw or add a picture of Stokes State Forest

Swartswood State Park

Swartswood

When did you visit?

Who came with you?

What did you do?

What was your favorite part?

Would you want to come back?

Draw or add a picture of Swartswood State Park

Tall Pines State Preserve

1705 Woodbury Glassboro Road, Wenonah

When did you visit?

Who came with you?

What did you do?

What was your favorite part?

Would you want to come back?

Draw or add a picture of Tall Pines State Preserve

Voorhees State Park

251 County Road Route 513, Glen Gardner

When did you visit?

Who came with you?

What did you do?

What was your favorite part?

Would you want to come back?

Draw or add a picture of Voorhees State Park

Warren Grove Recreation Area

Warren Grove

When did you visit?

Who came with you?

What did you do?

What was your favorite part?

Would you want to come back?

Draw or add a picture of Warren Grove Recreation Area

Washington Crossing State Park

355 Washington Crossing-Pennington Road, Titusville

When did you visit?

Who came with you?

What did you do?

What was your favorite part?

Would you want to come back?

Draw or add a picture of Washington Crossing State Park

Washington Rock State Park

44 Rock Road East, Green Brook

When did you visit?

Who came with you?

What did you do?

What was your favorite part?

Would you want to come back?

Draw or add a picture of Washington Rock State Park

WaWayanda State Park

885 Warwick Turnpike, Hewitt

When did you visit?

Who came with you?

What did you do?

What was your favorite part?

Would you want to come back?

Draw or add a picture of Wawayanda State Park

Wharton State Forest

Atlantic, Burlington and Camden Counties

When did you visit?

Who came with you?

What did you do?

What was your favorite part?

Would you want to come back?

Draw or add a picture of Wharton State Forest

Worthington State Forest

Old Mine Road, Columbia

When did you visit?

Who came with you?

What did you do?

What was your favorite part?

Would you want to come back?

Draw or add a picture of Worthington State Forest

Use this page for extra notes, drawings, and stickers

About the author, Jennifer Auer

Jennifer Auer is a married mom of three boys, who saw a need for a resource that helps families find affordable family fun in New Jersey. She founded Jersey Family Fun, LLC, to help families experience the best New Jersey has to offer. She is a hyperlocal blogger mom who uses her influence to plan events, spread social good and help small businesses and national brands reach her audiences.

Jennifer's creativity, blogging, management, organizational and social media skills have helped Jersey Family Fun become the premiere online destination for parents in New Jersey looking for ways to have fun with their children.

Jennifer has been a Jersey girl for 35 years, and a Jersey mom for 15 years. To work with or contact Jennifer Auer, please email jenniferauer@jerseyfamilyfun.com.

Encourage your kids to look for nature everywhere you go.
It's the weed breaking through the pavement,
It's the leaves forming small clumps along the side of the road.
It's the sky at any given time of the day or night.
It's the wind doing what it likes to your hair.
Look around, it won't take long to find it.
Penny Whitehouse

Please visit Jersey Family Fun at jerseyfamilyfun.com for more New Jersey kids activity books and things to do in New Jersey with kids.

Made in the USA
Middletown, DE
22 March 2022